LIFE WOULD BE FANTASTIC IF MY BRAIN DIDN'T *Boycott Me!*

A Quick Start Guide to Emotional Wellness
with Essential Oils and Mudras

Shahar Boyayan

547292

Printed in the United States of America

First Printing, 2015

ISBN 978-0-9907060-0-7

I'd like to thank my daughter Nashlah for being an amazing person, a big believer and my best friend.

CONTENTS

PREFACE

I started writing this book for myself. I was on a quest to find a way to tell my brain to stop boycotting me. I knew I had the potential to do it, to create and accomplish more than what I was achieving but every time I would try to get away from my current situation something would bring me back to step one.

It didn't matter if I was trying to make more money, lose weight or find the love of my life, I would advance a few steps and then would come back right to the beginning. Just like a crab at the beach, it seemed that I was always walking backwards. I am a driven person so I couldn't understand what was going on. I frequently blamed the economy, lack of healthy food, all good men are already married, and the list goes on.

One day a friend mentioned to me: "We are responsible for the situations we find ourselves in. We are the only ones to blame." It was then that I finally realized that unless I understood and embraced this concept nothing would change. You see, if we don't realize we are responsible for the results we get, there is no way we can create the change necessary to move forward. Intellectually I could accept this but still my actions were not taking me where I wanted to go.

I started studying the brain because I believed the answer was there. I needed to crack this code. I studied so much I became a Neuromarketer (a marketer that uses the unconscious part of the brain to reach consumers) and when I started applying these principles to my business, I started seeing results. I noticed that if I knew how to talk to the unconscious mind, positive things would start to happen.

I made the commitment to create a habit to communicate with my unconscious brain no matter how hard it would be, but my unconscious brain was set on keeping me where I was no matter what!

If I could show my unconscious brain a new reality and make the brain believe in it and if I could get rid of the fears that were not useful to me anymore, then everything would change and I would be able to achieve all of my goals.

At this point I knew enough about the brain to understand that affirmations and vision boards alone would not be enough. I knew the amygdala, which is part of the reptilian brain (unconscious part of the brain) is where fear is stored and does not respond to sound or images. I needed to find a new approach.

This was the moment that essential oils started to make a lot more sense to me because of their ability through arome to reach the amygdala. I then started combining them with affirmations and later with Mudras. Mudras are hand signs come from Pranayama yoga and are believed to send signals right to the brain through the use of pressure points.

I call this approach the **AromaPrana Technique**. When we combine essential oils, breathing techniques and Mudras to increase our emotional life force. As I started applying these methods, things started finally moving forward and I was able to live a new reality.

I am excited for you to experience the same results so you can also achieve your full potential.

Reaching your full potential is what this book is all about. This book will give you the knowledge to change your unconscious mind and to help you achieve what you want. If you will commit yourself to putting this information into practice and making a habit out of it, and keep doing it, you will see amazing results. This will not happen overnight, it will come with practice and repetition and it will bring a whole new path for you.

-Shahar

CHAPTER 1

Basics About the Brain and Our Emotions

We are going to get a little technical in this chapter. I want to explain to you how the brain works. It is not complicated once you understand the process your emotions go through and why it happens. This will then make a lot of sense when you are applying the techniques described in this book.

We were created for remarkable things, each and every one of us. Why do most of us find ourselves not having the ability to achieve our desires, repeating bad habits or simply not feeling worthy of acquiring the things we want? More often than not the solution is in our mind.

Each time the mind makes a decision about an event or feeling, it will try to create situations that will validate those feelings (whether they're good or bad). This chapter will show you how to release feelings and emotions that do not serve you, how to trigger your brain with the right stimuli, and how to live a happier life by combining essential oils, Mudras and breathing techniques. Simple things that can make a huge difference in your life, that by being applied and turned into positive habits, will help you become everything you were meant to be.

How the Mind Affects Your Feelings

Nowadays we are living in a world of emotional chaos. An increasing number of research[1] shows that our emotional well-being can have an extreme impact on our health and wellness. Research even shows that experiencing physical pain or sickness could be related to our emotions being out of balance. Now more than ever, many experts are under the impression that stressful emotional states impact the general health of the human body. A lot of articles mention[2] the probability that several ailments come from emotional troubles that link back to an early life, childhood–and furthermore even in the womb. These emotional challenges can jeopardize body systems and even impact other generations because it creates the equivalent of a molecular memory in fundamental parts and structures of the body. Desirable and undesirable events and ideas are recorded in our brain and confined into our memories all through our existence. These memories vary from minor, to overwhelming and have a gigantic impact on our well-being and happiness.

A lot is going on inside your mind. Your unconscious brain and its complicated systems are many times manipulating your thoughts. The unconscious part of your brain has a mission to keep you safe. For this part of the brain, safe means a situation it is comfortable and familiar with, even when it is a situa-

---

1   Baum, A. (1990). "Stress, Intrusive Imagery, and Chronic Distress," Health Psychology, Vol. 6, pp. 653-675.

2   http://goo.gl/S8PK6P
     http://goo.gl/lPQ4mE

tion that makes you feel miserable. Did you ever feel your life is like a crab walking? One step forward and two steps backwards? This is due to your unconscious brain. Every time you seek something different like losing weight, a business opportunity or going for dinner alone, the reptilian brain feels the need to protect you against the change which is unknown territory, and brings you back to its comfort zone. Many times this comfort zone is actually what you are trying to change. Your logical brain says you need to change something but the reptilian brain says "although she feels miserable here, here is safe and I'll keep her here".

Quite simply, there's considerably more behind that resentful emotion you get when a vehicle cuts you off. A lot is associated with interpreting these situations and creating your reactions to them. Your brain is influencing the way you feel, and how you react to those feelings in which you're most likely not even conscious of.

Although we consider emotions as inner states, psychologists define emotions as a combination of perceptions, feelings and actions. This suggests that what we think of as "emotions" involves not just how we feel, but also how we process and react to those feelings.

Our natural brain has not changed over the past 50,000 years and has only one role, to keep you safe. If in any situation this part of the brain perceives you not to be secure, it will use its incredible powers to keep you safe and secure. This could imply that although you may feel depressed, the brain understands this condition as a safe one and will try keep you in this stage.

Your mind is a sophisticated system that processes extensive amounts of information every moment. Belonging to the brain's information-processing network are neurons, or cells that broadcast receptions all through the brain. Neurons deliver signals via neurotransmitters, that are substances a few neurons release and others neurons receive. These chemical substances fundamentally allow the portions of the brain to correspond with one another.

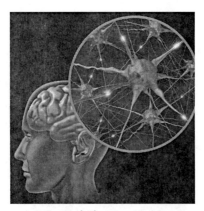

© Can Stock Photo Inc. / Eraxion

For instance, whenever you do something gratifying or pleasurable, the component of your brain that processes that data, interacts with the chemical dopamine. If your brain can't pick up dopamine naturally, the outcome is that you experience being significantly less delighted -- or maybe unhappy -- after what ought to have been a cheerful encounter.

Dopamine is a neurotransmitter which is produced by the brains of many living things, including humans. Dopamine has several different functions. It plays a critical role in the function of the central nervous system, and it is also linked with the brain's complex system of motivation and reward. Altered levels of dopamine in the brain can cause a range of symptoms and problems, like Attention Deficit Disorder[3], depression and rage.

Our feelings turn into chemical responses in our brain. Cells react to the things you express and believe. They document information and can even build neuro-pathways, and new highways of information. Body chemistry can become acidic and you need an alkaline body to stay healthy. When your body fluids contain too much acid, this is known as acidosis. Acidosis occurs when your kidneys and lungs can't keep your body's pH in balance.

Our human brain is comprised of a variety of parts that all function as a whole to process the information it receives. The primary section of the brain accountable for processing, the limbic system which is also called the reptilian brain, and is oftentimes known as the "emotional brain". We can reach the limbic system with the use images. An important part of the limbic system, referred to as the amygdala, evaluates the emotional benefit of stimuli. It's the primary part of the brain connected with anxiety reactions, which in-

---

3   http://goo.gl/yEQ0MX

cludes the "fight or flight" approach. An individual who has a seizure in the temporal lobe (the location of the amygdala) often times talks about an extreme feeling of dread or threat. **The amygdala does not react to visuals or sound, just to scent.** Consequently as a way to manage fearfulness the use of fragrances or aromas become very important.

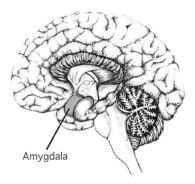

Amygdala

In the brain the hypothalamus is in charge of regulating how you react to emotions. When thrill or fear triggers your heart to beat faster, your blood pressure to surge, and your breathing to accelerate, it's the hypothalamus performing its duty. Another part of the brain, the hippocampus transforms your short-term memory into long-term memory and also assists you to restore saved memory. Your memories trigger how you respond to the world surrounding you, along with what your emotional reactions are going to be. Your memories become a map to your brain on how to react.

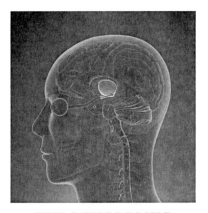

HYPOTHALAMUS

© Can Stock Photo Inc. / Eraxion

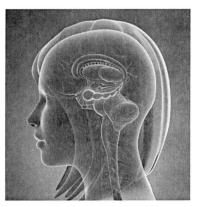

HIPPOCAMPUS

© Can Stock Photo Inc. / Eraxion

Since the two sides of your brain process information individually, they act together to hold your thoughts in balance. Here's an effective way to clarify it: the right hemisphere recognizes, and the left hemisphere interprets. The right brain detects disrupted energy flows, such as anxiety, rage or threat. It consequently signals the left brain, which determines how to pro-

ceed by reading the scenario and generating a rational choice on how to behave in response.

It's a terrific process, unless something occurs and
one area of the brain can't perform its task. Without
the left brain, the right brain would be overwhelmed
with depressing feelings rather than learn how to react to them. Furthermore, without the right brain, the
left brain is not going to be as good at recognizing
depressing thoughts.

Recognizing an adverse situation can leave you with an
awful temperament, and pondering on a happy memory can envelop you with a fantastic feeling. Research
also indicates that this impact is occurring regardless
of whether we're aware of the situation or not.

So what's the big deal? By using memory recall individuals can control their mood when enduring despair,
because pondering over positive memories motivates
the brain to generate dopamine. So we just have to
think positive right? When somebody tells you to liven
up, it could be as simple as wondering about joyful
memories. It is not that simple. You need to communicate with the amygdala in order to control anxiety
and fear. This is the reason you should incorporate
other stimulus such as aroma, breathing and touch.
A very important step that is quite often forgotten or
even unknown.

As you can imagine, recollections of earlier experiences affect the way you act in response to different
emotional scenarios. Let's suppose you had an earlier
situation where you almost drowned, now you might

experience fear around water for the rest of your life. If a former lover had a wandering eye, you may experience jealousy when your new companion looks at someone else. Even more, **the degree of the previous experience influences the intensity of the present emotion.** For instance, a person who may have had an intense traumatic encounter is most likely to show an extreme behavior soon after. This is quite common amongst soldiers.

Preconceived ideas additionally have an impact on your behavior. Your thoughts and expectations, which are powered by remembrances of past events, affect the intensity of an emotional feeling. As a way to gain emotional wellness we need to find out how to interact with our brain and instruct our mind to release our utmost capability. We are powerful beings and by becoming who we are supposed to become, we can change the lives of many. Why stay small when you can soar!

CHAPTER 2

How Can We Connect with our Brain?

We now know we can communicate with our primitive brain by means of imagery, we can interact with the amygdala by using aromas and we can speak to the left brain with words.

Our brain is fairly comparable to a computer system with plenty of links and pathways. We can utilize body stimuli and breathing to alter pathways which do not help us any longer. Similar to when you click the mouse in your computer and something different appears on the display screen. It is relatively a straightforward method, yet demands dedication on your part. Whenever we are dealing with emotions and harmful actions, persistence is vital, and the key to success. The more you do it, the more of the desirable outcome you will get.

Measures to emotional wellness:

In order *to transform any undesirable emotional structure we have to:*

1. **Identify and become conscious of what is in our way**. This phase can be rough but is really

crucial. We must connect with our suffering at its roots. We have to be aware of what is triggering the emotional issue. As I pointed out, it can be slightly distressful yet is key to the process. You don't want to try to fool yourself. If you really want to fix an issue a little discomfort while working on that issue may be necessary. The key is to catch yourself reacting when your emotions are triggered. Then you can discover if the threat is real or not.

This list includes some of the most common emotional triggers:

acceptance	be treated fairly	love
attention	be understood	new challenges
autonomy	be valued	order
balance	comfort	peacefulness
be in control	consistency	predictability
be liked	freedom	respect
be needed	fun	safety
be right	included	variety

Some of these needs will be important to you while others will have no emotional charge for you.

To start controlling your emotional triggers, choose three items from the list that most often set off your emotions when you don't get these needs met.

Be honest with yourself. Which will likely trigger a reaction in you?

The more you become attached to these needs, the more your brain will be on the lookout for circumstances that threaten your ability to have these needs met. Then your needs become emotional triggers.

At this point, you must judge the truth of the situation. If it's true that someone is ignoring your need or blocking you from achieving it, can you either ask for what you need or can you let the need go?

Without consciously acknowledging the need that is triggering the emotional reaction, we become enslaved to the need. On the other hand, if we honestly declare our needs we can begin to see life more objectively.

2. **Free that emotion.** This will require a commitment to let go of what is not helping us anymore. Get rid of it, say goodbye to old habits and thoughts that harm us.

Don't be afraid of your emotions. Don't fight them, run away from them or block them out. Welcome them, be with them, regardless of what they are. We were born with emotions. They are neither good or bad, they just are. Emotions dissipate and slowly disappear if you feel them, and are present with them. Just close your eyes and feel them as deeply as you can. You will learn more on how to free emotions that harm you in the next few chapters where we start implementing the AromaPrana technique.

There are 11 emotions that are considered toxic to us:

- ⊿ **Anger** – resentment, bitterness
- ⊿ **Guilt** – self-blame, false responsibility
- ⊿ **Greed** – insatiability, emotional hunger
- ⊿ **Fear** – anxiety, panic, immobilization
- ⊿ **Hate** – meanness, vengefulness
- ⊿ **Hopelessness** – loneliness, despair, desperation
- ⊿ **Hurt** – victimization, helplessness, blame
- ⊿ **Jealousy** – envy, possessiveness
- ⊿ **Pride** – better than, self-righteousness
- ⊿ **Sadness** – self-pity, regret
- ⊿ **Shame** – humiliation, embarrassment

3. **Move into a fresh reality.** Accept a whole new emotion or pattern, allow it to be a piece of your being and embrace your new personality. Pay attention to your outlook on life. You can either regret or rejoice; it's your choice.

Daily activities to help this process:

Be Thankful
Every day when you go to bed, find 3 things that occurred about your day that you are thankful for.

The idea behind this is that by being thankful for little things that happened, you are training your brain to see the positive side of life everywhere. Because these events really happened, your brain will not try to come back and say "This is not true, it is not real". It is very important to say what you are thankful for out loud.

I find it interesting in human nature that most of us condition our brain to see problems and the negative side every time something good happens to us. Don't believe me?

Let me give you a few examples:

Let's suppose you just got news that you were accepted to a University, got a new job or have become pregnant. At the very first moment you feel excitement, happiness, joy. Two seconds later you start thinking; Well, now I've to find a place to live, I don't know anybody there, need to buy new clothes, I don't like to be alone...... and here we go. We enjoyed happiness for a second or two and then started bringing doubt, concern and fear into the picture.

Ever experienced that? We don't allow ourselves to be happy, we feel happiness and then find ten thousand reasons to bury that feeling of happiness. Over time we train our brain to a point it is not able to recognize what happiness really is. It is this mystic feeling that lasts only a second or two. Yes, we cannot only blame the way our brain is wired on how we choose to handle emotions.

Keep a Journal
I'm not talking about a journal to write all your experiences like we did when we were teenagers. Simply write down one positive thing that happened during

that day that helped you move forward in one aspect of your life. Don't wait until end of the day because if you cannot think of one positive thing, you still have time to make it happen.

Write Down Your Goals
This has been tested many times. It works. Make a list of specific big goals you want to achieve.

For example: You want to make 1 million dollars every year or you want to travel to Africa or buy the house of your dreams.

Write all your goals down in a notebook every morning and every night that matter to you. Think big but be specific. Repeat this process every day.

Again we are creating a habit for the brain to go after our goals, to believe they are real and to see there is no threat in achieving them. You are also training yourself to be consistent and persistent. People that have studied great leaders have found that they all had rituals. Everyday rituals. Rituals become habits.

Be of Service
One of the best ways to train our brain not to focus on negative thoughts and feelings is to go and do something good to another person in need. Simple and effective. It also gives the brain some breathing time when it is not focusing on problems and then it actually allows the brain to find a solution.

There is one more thing that I found to be really helpful to me. It is a challenge that you can find on You-

Tube which started in Brazil. It is called "One Minute a Day."

The idea is that every day for one minute you will do something that is really uncomfortable for you.

For example:
- Pick up the phone and do a cold call.
- Jump from a plane- hopefully with a parachute.
- Join a group where you don't know anyone.

The goal is to do anything that you don't feel comfortable doing, and do it for at least one minute. You will be teaching your brain that you can get out of your comfort zone and you will still be safe. Therefore, telling your brain that change is a good thing.

For my daughter and I we use the term "Cross the Desert"

We live in Utah which has lots of deserts. Being from Brazil, I never thought I would have the opportunity to cross a desert. We are geocachers and we were doing a challenge some years ago of finding geocaches all around the state. Geocaching is a type of treasure hunting where the treasure you get is the trill of finding small containers hidden everywhere.

In order to complete this challenge, we had to cross a desert for the first time. We entered the desert all excited but forgot to bring water and we thought we would find restaurants in the desert, so we didn't bring food either. We were relying on a GPS that lost signal we were lost.

Yes, you can read and say "How Stupid" at the same time.

Our excitement faded and a lot of worries replaced that feeling. It took us about 4 hours to find a way out and when we did, we found ourselves in Nevada, a totally different state. A lot of feelings and thoughts crossed our minds during those hours. But afterwards, when all was well this amazing feeling came to both of us. A feeling that we had accomplished something major, something we never even considered possible. We had crossed a desert, a real desert, with sand, rock, crystals and in the middle of the summer with no one around. Maybe not the smartest thing to do but we felt invincible, we felt like we could do anything and that feeling was amazing!

So now, every other day or so we ask each other: "Have you crossed any deserts today?" and when one of us is trying to avoid something we feel uncomfortable doing we say: "Go cross your desert".

Yes, we need to remind ourselves how powerful we are and how far we can go because very often we tend to forget. We also need to have an anchor that leads us to that feeling when we are 100% sure that we really can accomplish anything. That is your "crossing the desert".

CHAPTER 3

Emotions

Emotions are fuels that can be switched and changed. Emotional balance methods are processes you carry out to soothe yourself when you are burdened or trapped in uncontrollable emotions. Also know in Human Behavior as: "modulate the emotions!" Don't be at the mercy of out-of-control feelings-learn to calm them down.

Everyone varies in their emotional responses due to different patterns in the central nervous systems and hormonal reactions to situations. Some individuals conquer depressing emotions quicker than others, while others have faster and stronger emotional reactions than others. Stronger negative thoughts may also take more time to recuperate from. If you grew up in a household where you did not feel supported, it might be more challenging for you to calm your emotions later in life when facing certain situations. In case you are more susceptible to negative thoughts, you can discover approaches to relax your inner thoughts and help you manage your sensitivity.

Affirmations combined with essential oils can be very beneficial. By using affirmations you are applying reciprocal inhibition, which simply means that two inner

thoughts cannot take up the similar space simultane-
ously. You cannot think about two different things at
the same time. You cannot feel hatred and joy at the
same time. When you focus on a favorable emotion,
the undesirable emotion will fade away.

Comfort and sensations of love and good self-esteem
help us escape from fear and anxiousness. Relaxation
rules! Good encounters switch on the pleasure centers
in the brain and lessen areas that identify discomfort.
When you find yourself furious, focus on emotions
like being calm, then the tension, sadness or rage
can lessen. The mind is resilient and can be managed
with the use of essential oils, affirmation, breathing
and Mudras.

Don't be a slave to your overpowering negative emotions. Your mind possesses the opportunity for change
as a result of the versatile character of your brain,
which changes and develops each time you uncov-
er new things. You can shield yourself against weak
thoughts of self-worth by taking charge of how you
react to situations.

CHAPTER 4

Breathing

Breathing is the initial and the final thing we do in life. It is what keeps us alive and oftentimes we take no notice of it, we simply breathe. Breathing is more than air going through the human body. The more mindful of your breathing you become, the better you can control your feelings.

Deep breathing supplies oxygen to your key organs and discharges impurities, including those brought on by tension. It also calms the nervous system and quiets those rapid thoughts, helping you to deal with anxiety and improve cognitive clarity.

The life span of animals depends on the number of breaths they take per minute. For example, a tortoise takes a breath once every three minute, its life span is around 300 years compared to a rabbit that takes a breath 45 times in a minute, it lives up to fifteen years, like this the breathing rate of the living species decides its life span[4]. By reducing the number of breaths we take one can extend a healthy life but this can only be achieved by regular practice of breathing exercises.

Breathe. Simply breathe. When feeling stressed or pressured, pause briefly and be aware of your breathing. Are you controlling your breath? Having extremely irregular breaths? Just observe. If you're holding your breath, start deliberately breathing in and out, to get a consistent flow going, not too intensely. If your breaths are shallow, gradually deepen by breathing through your nose, taking the breath down to your diaphragm and causing your tummy to enlarge. Next, gently breathe out, through the mouth if possible, but if that's overly noticeable in mixed company, exhale through the nose. Try if possible to pause and sit quietly, but if you don't have time to stop whatever you're doing, rest for a couple seconds, just long enough to build a calm and consistent breathing pattern, then resume your activity while still focusing on breathing. The stress will lessen and you'll feel more peaceful and clear-headed and ready to concentrate on the task taking place.

Here are a few breathing techniques to be applied:

Box Breathing - This approach aids when the hamster wheel in your head just won't stop whirling. Inhale an extended, deliberate, deep breath while mentally counting to four and hold your breath four counts, then breathe out while counting to four. The breathing calms the body while the counting helps divert the mind from a compulsive state to a contemplative one by providing the brain an alternative focus. This works well when you have being mentally debating over and over with a choice you need to make but you can't come to a decision. It contributes greatly to switch focus, take a break and re-invigorate.

Tension Release - Regardless if its work, stress or personal life trials, there's a saturation stage where enough is enough and all that mental vitality centered on the past is robbing you of living in the present. To help release the tension, sit or stand in a relaxed position. Slowly inhale through your nose, mentally counting to five then exhale through your mouth, counting to eight as it leaves your lungs. Repeat several times.

Tips:
As you breathe, let your abdomen expand outward, rather than raising your shoulders. This is a more relaxed and natural way to breathe, and helps your lungs fill themselves more fully with fresh air, while releasing more "stale" air.
You can repeat a few times to release tension, or for several minutes as a form of meditation.

Creating harmony - Sit in a meditative pose or in a comfortable position on the floor.

1. Keep your back straight, shoulder muscles relaxed and close your eyes.
2. Close both ears with the index fingers on both hands.
3. Raise your elbows to shoulder height.
4. Inhale deeply.
5. Hold your breath for as long as possible.
6. Exhale slowly making a buzzing sound like that of a bee.

Hissing - Breathe deeply in through the nose and then exhale through the mouth. On the release, pucker the lips while they are slightly open, then pull them back as if you're grinning. This truly aids in irritation. The hissing sound that results when pulling back the mouth is an efficient release of emotion.

Purify - Sit comfortably with your spine straight and shoulders relaxed. Keep a gentle smile on your face, place your left hand on the left knee, palms open to the sky with your thumb and index finger gently touching at the tips.

Place the tip of the index finger and middle finger of the right hand in between the eyebrows, the ring finger and little finger on the left nostril, and the thumb on the right nostril. We will use the ring finger and little finger to open or close the left nostril and thumb for the right nostril.

Press your thumb down on the right nostril and breathe out gently through the left nostril. Now breathe in from the left nostril and then press the left nostril gently with the ring finger and little finger, while removing the right thumb from the right nostril, and then breathe out through the right nostril. Breathe in from the right nostril and exhale from the left. Continue inhaling and exhaling from alternate nostrils.

Complete nine such rounds by alternately breathing through both the nostrils. After every exhalation, remember to breathe in from the same nostril from which you exhaled. Keep your eyes closed and continue taking long, deep, smooth breaths without any force or effort.

CHAPTER 5

Conquering Limiting Beliefs

How do we re-train our brain?

With a purpose to attain emotional abundance and re-train our brain to achieve a more constructive result we are going to employ 4 elements:

1. Breathing techniques
2. Essential oils
3. Mudras
4. Affirmations

The brain needs to accept a different present than the one it lives in, so again, be consistent.

Conquering Limiting Beliefs

The stronger your values, the more they appear un-shakeable, and the more you will discover proof to support them.

What most individuals don't recognize is that the vast majority of our beliefs concerning the world are not really real. They are true because we've determined they are. Some are just illusions of who we really are.

Beliefs are shaped through recurring imagination, and are part of you because you have chosen or consented that they are real.

Here are a number of collective limiting beliefs that you've most likely agreed to:

- Having Money is filthy
- People are dishonest
- Time is money
- Once you're a grown-up, life is about work, not fun
- Dreams don't come true

In addition to these there are possibly plenty of personally acquired limiting beliefs you've gathered through your personal experiences. Whatever the situation, most beliefs are shaped unconsciously, without our awareness about it. We didn't necessarily plan to approve these values because we desired to.

It's not like one day we woke up and imagined "Girl, you know what would be awesome? To go out today and replicate a bunch of ideas that are likely to become fast opinions that will hold me from enjoying the life I want. Yeah, I think that's what I'll accomplish today." That would not be a smart thing to do

None of us wish to keep these beliefs, but we either consider:

1. That's simply the way things have always been (everybody else confirms), or...

2. It started to be such a part of my personality that it's too difficult to change now.

To be able to resolve these limiting beliefs, we must understand that what is frequently viewed as "just the way things are" is just a combined theory. And since it's a theory, that means that we chose to agree to create that theory as well, on some conscious or unconscious level. So to fix this, we need to revive our energy and decide to quit committing to this pattern. It can truly be that easy.

Usually these limiting beliefs can be quite difficult to alter. Because we're so accustomed to them and because we identify with them, they maintain plenty of weight in our lives. They can seem like immovable objects on our path.

A few typical limiting beliefs are...

- ⅄ The emotion of not being smart enough
- ⅄ The feeling of not being good enough
- ⅄ Needing to fight for money
- ⅄ Not worthy of getting things
- ⅄ [insert your limiting belief here]

These things can appear intimidating when we try to change. Perhaps even when you do create a genuine, constant effort, inertia is commonly just too difficult to beat. It is what I call "The gap of no guarantee".

We can be stuck in this gap forever. Here is why. If you have a job you know that every month you will get paid. It is guaranteed. So you work (actions) and you get rewarded (money). You know you will always get the money so every single action you do while working is guarantee. You feel safe. But if you had to work not knowing if you would get paid or not, what would you do?

When we try to change a pattern in our behaviors or emotions we are not sure of what will happen or who we will become. The result is not granted. A good result is not granted. There is no guarantee. So we stay in the gap and don't take action. Nothing changes, but we feel safe.

Fortunately, there are several measures you can take to make the shift, further empowering values.

1. **Avoid identifying yourself with your beliefs.**
   Most beliefs are extremely challenging to modify because we identify with them. They appear to be ingrained as an element of who we are. And given that we identify with them, we permit ourselves to be defined by them. If you believe you're not artistic, you'll find yourself as a person who just wasn't blessed with that skill. If you feel you're terrible fixing things, you might think you're just not a technical individual. It's simple to get caught up in letting our beliefs define us, but they don't have to. Therefore the initial step is to avoid identifying with or defining yourself according to what you believe.

2. **Question your opinions.**
   Whatever you imagine you know to be certain may perhaps be considerably more flexible than

you imagine. What you consider to be expected is certain to be much more negotiable. Question all of the findings you have as to what you believe to be real, fixed or achievable.

3. **Review your assumptions.**
   Without forcing the limit and testing your assumptions, it's difficult to shift past your limiting beliefs. You need to do something to crack the pattern of your limiting belief. Questioning is the starting point, however if you only do that, the chances of shifting to a more empowering mindset stay in your mind. Some type of activity must be taken that puts your conclusions to the test. Ensure that you're not living in the restricted head-space that leads you to boost what you already possess to be real. Dismiss your judgment and take a solid step to analyze your assumptions.

Perhaps it will sound too simple, however these are the measures to moving past any limiting belief. They're only part of it, though. To help you to truly incorporate a fresh, more empowering belief, you'll need to spend time nurturing it.

CHAPTER 6

Essential Oils

The supportive benefits of essential oils can be unique. They can influence healing on all four realms of reality - physical, mental, emotional and spiritual.

The body's healing systems constitute more than the natural immunity alone. Though valuable, the immune system is just one side of the body's entire healing system consisting of the delicate body, the psyche and nervous system, the endocrine glands, and others. All function as a whole to assist and preserve well-being.

How Do Essential Oils Influence Our Minds and Our Emotions?

Essential oils have an effect on our thoughts and our feelings. All aromas have a possible emotional impact that can get deep into the mind.

Our sense of smell is projected to be 10,000 times more powerful than our other senses. Aromas travel to the brain faster than vision or noise. Every time we breathe in the scent of an essential oil, the chemical compounds travel through the nose where they're registered by the senses of the olfactory membranes in the nose lining. The odor molecules stimulate this lining of nerve tissues and provoke electrical stimulation to the olfactory bulb in the brain. The olfactory bulb then transports the impulses to the amygdala - where emotional memories are kept - and to other areas of the limbic system of the brain.

> *"Because the limbic system is directly connect-ed to those parts of the brain that control heart rate, blood pressure, breathing, memory, stress levels, and hormone balance, essential oils can have profound physiological and psychologi-cal effects. Olfactory responses to odors induce the brain to stimulate the release of hormones and neurochemicals that in turn alter the body's physiology and behavior."*
> *-Essential Oil Desk Reference, 4th Edition*

The limbic lobe is a group of brain structures posi-tioned directly below the cerebral cortex of the brain and comprises of the hippocampus and the amygdala. It's designed for instantly revitalizing the hypothal-amus - typically known as the "master gland." This gland is one of the most important components of the brain and acts as the hormonal regulation cen-ter. The hypothalamus discharges hormones that can change everything from sexual urge to energy levels. The generation of growth hormones, sex hormones, thyroid hormones, and neurotransmitters such as se-rotonin, are generally governed by the hypothalamus.

Due to their aroma and distinct molecular framework, essential oils can instantly encourage the limbic lobe and the hypothalamus. Inhalation of essential oils enables you to relieve tension and emotional crisis. It can also serve to activate some hormones from the hypothalamus.

The Emotional Brain Reacts Merely to Aroma

The section of the brain referred to as the amygdala performs a significant function in keeping and eliminating emotional distress. The only approach to communicate to this gland is with aroma or by means of the sense of smell. Quite simply - the emotional mind responds merely to aroma and not to words that are read, voiced, heard, or sensed by Braille. Our sense of smell links straight to emotional states and actions commonly preserved since our childhood.

Smell is the only one of the five bodily senses that is directly connected to the limbic lobe of the brain - our emotional control center. Anxiousness, despair, worry, rage, and enjoyment all literally originate from this section. A particular scent can stimulate recollections and inner thoughts before we are even deliberately aware of it. Each time smells are involved, we respond initially and think after words.

All other physical senses are diverted through the thalamus, which acts as the switchboard for the brain, transmitting stimuli onto the cerebral cortex (the conscious thought center) and other areas of the mind.

Essential oils allow us to pick up collected or neglected moments and restrained emotions so that we can accept and implement or emit them. The term "emotions" can translate as "energy-in-motion." Emotion is

the experience of energy traveling through our system. This emotional power functions at a greater pace
than thought. Thought and visuals can take seconds
or minutes to stir up a memory while a smell can stimulate a memory in milliseconds.

Abandoned memories and suppressed emotions can
bring chaos in our existence; usually being the source
behind the despair, stress and uncertainties. Essential
oils can help us surface and discharge these emotions
wherever they are kept in the body or energy field.
They're primarily helpful when used with breathing
techniques and hand stimuli- the Mudras.

Do Essential Oils Work With Emotions?

Everyone thinks that our psychological and rational
states rule our physical body. As a result, the true
work must begin at the root; quite simply, at the mental and emotional stages.

Removing an energy obstacle demands determining
the underlying emotions, recognizing the pattern, and
particularly learning the lesson—so as to prevent a
repetition of the similar routine. Until we gain knowledge from an experience, we carry on repeat behavior
patterns. Related scenarios from the past will often
resurface; many can be unveiled simply by acknowledging them, others need much more effort. If you
tend to say: "This always happens to me" you are
living this pattern.

High frequency essentials oils can unlock the subconscious entries and disengage the obstacles that keep us from eliminating our traumas. The oils oxygenate the cells and bring its blockages to the surface, so that they can be eliminated.

Essential Oil molecules are the tiniest molecules of all matter (lower than 500 atomic bulk units.) Some essential oils even have the power to permeate the Blood-Brain Barrier. When you breathe in oil molecules into the back passages of your nose, they go directly to the central part of the brain called the amygdala, the headquarters of the limbic system.

This method is the section of your brain that handles the storage and filing system for all your emotional experiences, just like the file administrator in your computer manages your computer's records.

Any time we have an emotional experience, specially a distressing or unpleasant one, the amygdala assigns a part of your body to recall that experience until you are prepared to cope with it.

Because every organ of the human body carries a certain vibrational frequency, and so does each emotion, the amygdala transmits the emotion to be filed to an area in our body that complements the particular vibrational frequency of that particular emotion. That is why we carry anger obstructions in the liver, stress in the stomach and fear blockages in the kidneys and so on. Those feelings that are not handled, at some point, will resurface, to provide us one more opportunity to learn from it. Moreover, the blockages kept in our organs, glands and systems, reduce our bodily vibrational regularity. When our physical vibrational frequency falls below a particular level, illness may arise.

Essential oils hold electrical charges, typically electrons or negatives ions, which are therapeutic and beneficial. Essential oils are also vibrant. They build nanovolts of electricity (billionths of a volt) at megahertz frequencies (that's in the radio frequency range of millions of cycles per second). For example: Rose oil has a frequency of 320 MHz, the highest frequency of all known substances.

The normal frequency of the human body during the daytime is 62-68 Mhz. A sound frequency is 62-72 MHz.

Another important element to look at is the chemistry of essential oils. Although the chemical makeup of an essential oil is quite intricate for us to analyze here, there are two aspects of this chemistry that perform a substantial task in our healing work. They are Sesquiterpenes and Monoterpenes.

Sesquiterpenes
Sesquiterpenes   remarkable   anti-inflammatory attributes have recently been under critical study. Researches on sesquiterpenes related to cancer, uncovers that they can also get rid of or re-write miswritten codes in the DNA. Once more, a probability that we cannot ignore using essentials oils for energy work purposes. Re-writting miswritten codes in the DNA might be all that it is needed for an

efficient elimination of cellular blockage. Oils high in sesquiterpenes are:

- ⅄ Black Pepper (30%)
- ⅄ Myrrh (39%)
- ⅄ Ylang Ylang (40%)
- ⅄ Cedarwood (50%)
- ⅄ Patchouli (50%)
- ⅄ Ginger (55%)
- ⅄ Sandalwood 90%

Monoterpenes

Monoterpenes are some of the most compact molecules in aromatherapy, which travels quickly to the nose, and extremely fast to evaporate. The majority of the citrus oils fall under the high monoterpene category.

- ⅄ Eucalyptus (30%)
- ⅄ Lemon (87%)
- ⅄ Orange (90%)
- ⅄ Grapefruit (96%)

Others oils also high in monoterpene are:

- ⅄ Galbanum (80%)
- ⅄ Angelica (73%)
- ⅄ Hyssop ((70%)
- ⅄ Peppermint (45%)
- ⅄ Juniper (42%)
- ⅄ Frankincense (40%)
- ⅄ Spruce (38%)
- ⅄ Pine (30%)

Other than their wide range of health improving capabilities, they can reprogram miswritten information in the cellular memory, making essential oils rich in monoterpenes ideal for use in energy work, while flushing old thoughts or emotional habits.

Essential oils encourage the secretion of antibodies, neurotransmitters, endorphins, hormones, and enzymes in the human body. They are active chemically and electrically. Essential oils have the ability to secure favorable energy and align it with each person's distinctive emotional coding.

Which Essential Oils to Use for Emotional Well-Being

It is very important that you only use high quality essential oils. Therapeutic grade essential oils. Do not use any oils topically if they are not therapeutic grade.

Here is a snippet of essential oils and their use with emotions:

Cedarwood
- clears thoughts of countless forms but specifically blockages related to pride.
- Aids with fear

Bergamot
- Encourages self-esteem.
- Ease agression
- Aids with grief

Cypress
- Supports individuals who are trapped or dormant in life.
- Can lead to release emotions
- Supports inner thoughts to flow again.
- Aids giving voice to expression of emotions
- Position on the kidneys (which is in charge of the movement of fluids in the body), water symbolizing emotions and assisting our emotions to circulate again

Geranium
- Emotional healer
- Carries strong resonance with the heart
- Beneficial to preparing a mother for childbirth
- Suitable for individuals whose heart has been wounded
- Great for inner child work
- Enable discomfort to disappear
- Aids with panic
  Place one to two drops on the heart

Grapefruit
- Supports the body
- Aids in reducing food desires
- Assists us to pay attention to the refined messages of our body and to respect our body

Lavender
- Calms worries
- Gives you determination and strength
- Aids us to speak our truth
  Place one to drops on the throat

Lemon
- Serves to support the left brain (i .e. the analytical brain).
- It is the oil of focus
- Aids with aggression
  Set it on the right side of the body.

Lemongrass
- Excellent for individuals who are upset
  Place one to two drops over the liver (the center for rage)

Lime
- Supports the heart
- purifies issues with the heart;
- helps to eliminate sorrow.
  Place one or two drops on the heart center.

Myrrh
- Connection with the earth and our birth mother.
- Beneficial oil to place on babies feet shortly after they are born.
- Calm emotions
- uplifting

Marjoram
- Suitable for individuals who are aloof and closed off in the heart center and from life
- Helps individuals to attach in depth with life.
- Helps with loneliness
- Aids with grief

Lavender

⅄ Tension

⅄ Suspicion

⅄ Shock and panic

Peppermint

⅄ Shyness

⅄ Emotional Fatigue

⅄ Jealousy

Ylang-Ylang

⅄ Anger

⅄ Aggression

⅄ Emotional fatigue

⅄ Nervousness

⅄ Sexual blocks

⅄ Stress

CHAPTER 7

Mudras

A Mudra (Sanskrit term which means symbol or seal) is a gesture or position, typically of the hands, that fastens and leads energy flow and reflexes to the brain. By curling, crossing, stretching and touching the fingers and hands, we can "talk" to the body and mind as each section of the hand corresponds to a particular part of the mind or body.

Cerebral activity is initialized and trained by touching and feeling, especially with the fingertips. When Mudras are exercised deliberately, which implies that we concentrate on our fingers and whatever they are resting on, they stimulate large areas of the brain through the meridians.

From the pinky finger to the thumb: each finger signifies earth, metal, fire, wood, and water, respectively. The whole world remains within your ten fingers and I find it amazing that there are a great variety of Mudras although we only have 10 fingers. Mudras works extremely well for emotional wellness. Mudras activate selected areas of the brain and exercise a corresponding effect on these areas. Mudras can be carried out while seated, in lying position, standing, or even walking.

Be certain that your body posture is symmetrical and centered, and that you are as peaceful as possible. If you sit on a chair while doing them, your back must be straight and both feet requires full contact with the floor.

Begin each Mudra session by "washing" your palms (rub your hands back and forth against each other about 10 times, hold your open hands in front of your navel) this will assist energy to stream from your hands. In each Mudra, exert adequate pressure to feel the flow of energy but not enough to whiten fingertips.

As described above your fingers correspond to emotions and the major organs. The meridians run on the inside and outside of your fingers (not top to bottom!) which also have various acupuncture points positioned in them.

By pushing or squeezing the sides of the fingers, in accordance with your preferences, you can influence both the emotion and the corresponding organ.

This is how the fingers work:

• **The thumb** corresponds to the element earth, the stomach and worry .
• **The index finger** represents the element metal, the lungs, the large intestine and the emotions depression, sorrow and misery.
• **The middle finger** is the element fire, the heart, small intestine, circulatory and respiratory systems and the emotions of impatience and boldness.

• **The ring finger** is the element wood and is linked to the liver, gall bladder, nervous system and corresponds to anger.
• **The pinky finger** symbolizes water, the kidneys and fear.

So if you are overwhelmed by an emotion, simply squeeze the corresponding finger a few times and you will feel better. It truly does work!

Abhaya Varada Mudra
Place your right hand cupped in front of tummy with palm facing up. Hold left hand with palm forward in front of the left shoulder.
Benefits: Instills boldness and fearlessness.
Practice Tips: Work with when feeling nervous.

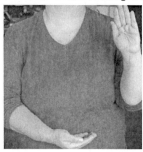

Avhana Mudra

Place sides of palms against each other, little fingers touching, press thumbs into base of index finger, hold other fingers together; place hands on your chest.

Benefits: Enhances capability to receive, respiration
Practice Tips: Use with difficulty accepting aid from others.

Bhairava Mudra

Rest cupped left hand in cupped right hand; rest hands in the lap.

Benefits: Encourages a sense of surrender and serenity.
Practice Tips: Use when feeling worry or tension.
Warnings: Don't do this Mudra if you have low blood pressure.

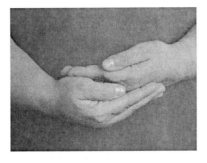

Garuda Mudra

Cross the left wrist in front of the right wrist and interlace the thumbs together, spread the other fingers apart in front of the upper chest.

Benefits: Regulates the right and left sides of the body, generates a feeling of independence.

Practice Tips: Use when you feel trapped in your life or emotions.

Warnings: Don't do this Mudra if you have high blood pressure use caution and monitor.

Hansi Mudra

Touch tips of all fingers together apart from the pinkie fingers. Hold hands out to the side of the body with extended pinkies pointing upwards.

Benefits: Launches inner smile and thoughts of fulfillment.

Practice Tips: Use when feeling gloomy or lonesome.

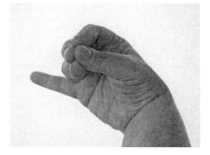

Jalashaya Mudra

Interlace thumb, index and middle fingers from both hands while keeping the ring and pinkie fingers long and extended together. Hold hands at the abdomen with fingers pointing away from body.

Benefits: Cools and calms the body and mind.

Practice Tips: Helpful for intense emotions of prudence and fury.

Kaleswara Mudra

Start with palms together. Bend all of your fingers toward each other until your knuckles are touching, then extend the middle fingers while keeping fingertips together while putting the palms away from each other. Draw thumb points toward body.

Benefits: Increases self-esteem.

Practice Tips: Use with all addictions.

Kapota Mudra
Place with palms together. Build room between palms maintaining finger tips, thumbs and heels of hands together; hold at the heart.
Benefits: Stimulates the heart center.
Practice Tips: Use when stressed out.
Warnings: Don't do this Mudra if you have a headache.

Medha Prana Kriya Mudra
Touch index finger nails to the middle joint of the thumb and apply light pressure, extend all other fingers and turn palms up.
Benefits: Opens heart and emits deep emotional blockages.
Practice Tips: Use when feeling overwhelmed by old emotional patterns.
Warnings: Those medicated for psychological situations.

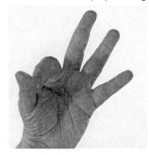

Padma Mudra

Place hands together at the heart, hold thumbs and little fingers together, open other fingers and create cup shape between palms.

Benefits: Raises heart energy, integrates body and mind.

Practice Tips: Use to heal your emotional heart.

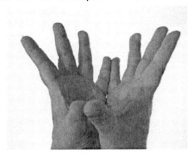

Pala Mudra

Softly cup both hands. Hold the left hand palm upwards below the navel. Hold the right hand palm downwards above the navel.

Benefits: Results in a sense of trust and wholeness. Ideal for anxiety.

Practice Tips: Use yo heal your emotional heart

Prajna Prana Kriya

Use both hands. Touch index finger nail to lowest joint of thumb and apply light pressure, extend all other fingers and turn palms up.

Benefits: Slows breath, discharges deep stress

Practice Tips: Survival stressors, extreme tension.

Warnings: low blood pressure.

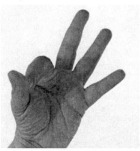

Pushan Mudra

Right Hand: Touch tips of thumb, index & middle fingers together while extending ring and pinky fingers.

Left Hand: Touch tips of thumb, middle & ring fingers together, while extending index and pinky fingers. Rest hands on legs with palms up.

Benefits: initiates relaxation response.

Practice Tips: Use when you feel like you are internalizing the stressors in your life.

Pushpaputa Mudra

Cup hands with pinky fingers together and ring fingertips touching each other creating a bowl shape.
Benefits: Empathy, kindness, giving.
Training Tips: Use as an offering to someone you love.

Shanka Mudra

Hold left thumb with right hand. Wrap left fingers around right fits and touch right thumb to left index finger.
Benefits: Provides a feeling of sanctuary.
Practice Tips: Use with low self-worth or fear.

Vaikhara Mudra
Make a fist with thumbs on outside of fingers then cross forearms over chest with right arm closest to body.
Benefits: Sense of security and confidence.
Practice Tips: Use with low self-worth or fearfulness.
Warnings: High Blood Pressure.

Vajra Mudra
Touch the tips of the thumbs and index fingers together then bring the right hand and left hands together and join the joined thumbs and index fingers as well as the tips of the middle fingers together . Let the ring and pinkie fingers curl softly inward. Hold the hands at the chest.
Benefits: Releases energy and vigorousness.
Practice Tips: Helpful for despair.

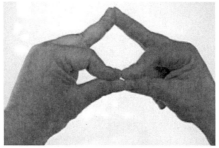

Vajrapradama Mudra

Clasp fingers of both hands and open palms toward heart; point thumbs upwards. Hold a few inches away from the chest.

Benefits: Develops confidence, security, opens the heart.

Practice Tips: Use when terrified or troubled.

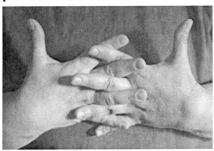

Kubera Mudra

Place thumb, index and middle fingers together while bending the ring and pinky fingers towards the palm

Benefits: Fixation on the essential and passing through new gateways.

Practice Tips: Apply it if you wish to put more pressure behind your plans for the future.

Ksepana Mudra

Palms together, index finger touching each other and pointing upwards. Thumbs crossing each other, middle, ring finger and pinky fingers crossing each other. This Mudra inspires expended or harmful energy to flow away, followed by the absorption of pure and positive energy.

Benefits: If you have an emotional outburst due to some bad experience or if you feel you have no energy or if life seems unfair to you – practice Ksepana Mudra for two minutes and charge your body with positive energy.

Practice Tips: removes the negative energy from the body

Hakini Mudra

Hold your hands up in front of you, so that your palms face each other, but do not touch. Bring the fingertips of your right hand towards the fingertips of your left hand so that they are touching each other.

When it comes to science, this finger position has been studied fairly well; experts have identified that it encourages the cooperation between the right and left brain hemispheres. It is also advisable today in memory workouts and management classes. It is said to open access to the right hemisphere, which is where the memory is kept. This Mudra also enhances and deepens respiration, and the brain gains from it as well.

Benefits: Improvement in concentration and memory
Promotion of coordination between the left and right hemispheres of the brain
Creation of a sense of calmness, which opens the mind to clearer thinking.

Practice tips: Practice these steps several times. The hakini mudra is useful when you have forgotten something momentarily and wish to recollect it.

Tse Mudra

Sit in a comfortable position. Spine should be erect. Place both the hands on your thighs. Place the tip of the thumb on the base of your little finger as indicated in the picture. Now encircle the thumb with the four fingers.

Culture claims that this Mudra chases away sorrow, lessens anxiety, turns away failure and bad fortune, and overcomes depressions. It is known to improve personal attraction and enrich the instinctive and mental powers.

Benefits: Good for depression, increases magnetism, develops mental ability, sharpens intuition and let you get rid of depression.

Practice Tips: Do this exercise for minimum of 7 times and for a maximum of 49 times.

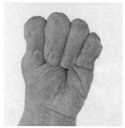

CHAPTER 8

Putting It All Together & AromaPrana Protocols

Here you will find some basic protocols.

They include essential oils, the respective Mudra and breathing techniques with affirmations.

Choose the issue you want to work on and apply the protocol for at least seven days. Once you experience a shift, then move to another one.

The protocols below are for topical and aromatic use. For topical use I like to combine the oils in a roll-on bottle so I can carry with me any time and use at least 3 times a day. I add fractionated coconut oil to the essential oils and apply on my forearm unless otherwise instructed.

AromaPrana Emotional Wellness Protocols

Don't utilize all the protocols concurrently.The majority of us have various emotional concerns we wish to change, however, it is crucial that you deal with one issue at a time, and then another and then another. When trying to re-train our brain and adjust behavior it is one move and one emotion at a time. By changing the way you react to one emotion you will also be changing other reactions. So wait to finish one process before starting another. It pays to be patient here. Keep the commitment to focus on one solution for at least seven days before moving on to another one. Some concerns will take longer because it will take sometime for the brain to see the new reality and accept it as true.

Being present in the moment
⋏ Use Frankincense, Wild Orange and Cypress to come to the present moment.

Fear
⋏ 7 drops Clove
⋏ 5 drops Clary Sage
⋏ 3 drops Juniper
⋏ 3 drops Cypress
⋏ 3 drops Ginger
⋏ 2 drops Fennel. Add to a diffuser.

Breath: Deep breathing.
Mudra: Bhairava Mudra

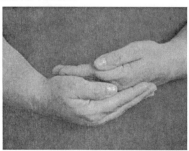

Affirmation: "I am capable and strong. I am not my fears"

Grief
- 5 drops of Geranium
- 10 drops of Lime
- 15 drops Roman Chamomile
- 7 drops Cypress

Breathe: Tough Emotions.
Mudra: Padma Mudra.

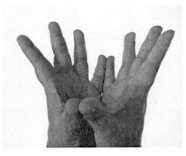

Affirmation: "Mourning is a part of life and I'm surviving."

Depression
- 10 drops of Peppermint
- 3 drops of Basil
- 2 drops of Rosemmary
- 3 drops of Geranium

Back of neck, throat and sternum.
Breathe: Create Peace.
Mudra: Vradja Mudra.

Affirmation: "Each day I am finding myself happier."

Accept Wealth & Abundance
- ⅄ 4 drops Wild Orange
- ⅄ 2 drops Cinnamon
- ⅄ 3 drops Frankincense
- ⅄ 1 drop Rose

Breathe: Breathe Deeply.
Mudra: Kubera Mudra.

Affirmation: "Wealth flows easily to me."

Guilt
- ⅄ 3 drops of lemon
- ⅄ 2 drops of bergamot

⚶ 1 drop of peppermint
Breathe: Hissing
Mudra: Kapota

Affirmation: I am accepting of all abundant things coming into my life

Feeling stuck

⚶ 2 drops lemongrass
⚶ 3 drops cypress
⚶ 1 drop fennel
⚶ 1 drop thyme
Breathe: Create peace
Mudra: Vajrapradama

Affirmation: I always move forward

Self- Acceptance
⅄ 3 drops of Bergamot
⅄ 3 drops of Grapefruit
Breathe: deep breathing
Mudra: Padma

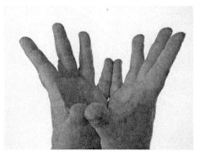

Affirmation: I accept myself and I allow growth

Anger
⅄ 2 drops Geranium
⅄ 2 drops Ylang Ylang
⅄ 1 drop Thyme
Breathe: deep breathing
Mudra: Garuda

Affirmation: I control my emotions

FINAL THOUGHTS

This is just the beginning . As you experience another reality you will see your true potential.

There are many more essential oils that can empower you emotionally as well as other Mudras. This is just the start of a journey. A journey that you will thoroughly enjoy!

Disclaimer: I'm not a doctor nor a therapist and I'm not clamming these techniques can cure diseases. I'm only sharing with you my own experience and studies. You are responsible for your own actions.

ADDITIONAL RESOURCES

⅄ AromaPrana Certification

⅄ Class Charts

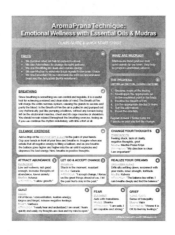

www.OilBusinessMastery.com

ABOUT THE AUTHOR

Shahar Boyayan is a marketer by trade and she specializes in NeuroMarketing which basically is selling to emotions.

She has always being fascinated by the brain and how emotions work.

In Brazil where she is originally from she studied psychology and as a trainer has given dozens of courses on Neurolinguistic.

But she always felt the need for a more specific way when dealing with emotions. Something that could be applied by anyone on a regular basis. After all, consistency is the key to success in any endeavor.

Also because she felt that a more effective way of talking to the unconscious brain was needed.

She started using essential oils personally and then started studying Mudras in Pranayama Yoga.

The oils talking to the amygdala where fears and emotions are stored and the Mudras send signals to the brain and the whole body made a lot of sense.

She saw incredible results in her own life and when she added the right type of breathing, it was like a perfect storm.

Great results can be achieved by this approach.

She decided to write this book in order to share her new passion on Emotional Wellness with essential oils, Mudras and breathing.